Flowers
colour by
numbers

Flowers
colour by numbers

Else Lennox

ARCTURUS

ARCTURUS

This edition published in 2016 by Arcturus Publishing Limited
26/27 Bickels Yard, 151–153 Bermondsey Street,
London SE1 3HA

Illustrations copyright © Else Lennox
Design copyright © Arcturus Holdings Limited

ISBN: 978-1-78404-979-9
CH004968NT
Supplier 29, Date 0316, Print Run 4940

Printed in China

Created for children 10+

INTRODUCTION

Whether in country meadows, gardens or city window boxes, flowers always bring a welcome dash of colour to our lives. With this fantastic collection of colour-by-number images you can explore the beauty of flowers and develop your colouring skills at the same time.

There is a guide to the colours to use, and you should match them to your own pencils as closely as you can – perhaps label each pencil with the correct key number to make it easier to see which is which. From bright greens, through pinks, oranges, purples and blues, to dark, velvety browns, explore nature's colours in all their variety.

If there is no number that means that space should be left white – or, if you wish, you can fill it in with white pencil. By carefully colouring between the lines, the flowers will grow and appear before your eyes – you will be planting by numbers!

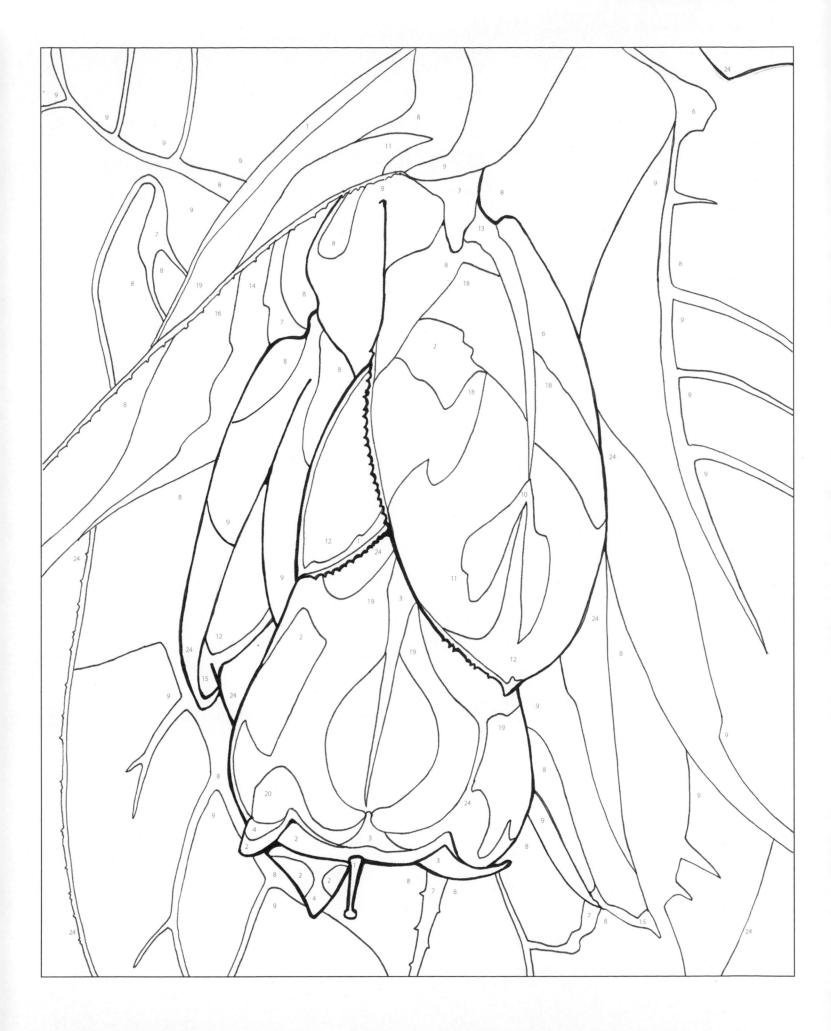